# You can be
# Princess Catherine's
# Bridesmaid

For Charlotte,

   Our very own
princess I hope you
enjoyed the big day
      lots of love
      Auntie Sam XX
            X

First published in Great Britain in 2011 by Piccadilly Press Ltd,
5 Castle Road, London NW1 8PR
www.piccadillypress.co.uk

All photos copyright Rex Features
Designed by Simon Davis
Printed and bound in Italy by Printer Trento srl
Colour reproduction by Imagewrite Ltd

ISBN: 978 1 84812 181 2 (paperback)

1 3 5 7 9 10 8 6 4 2

A catalogue record of this
book is available from
the British Library

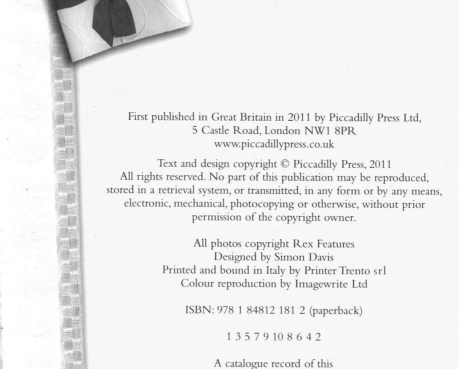

MIX
Paper from
responsible sources
FSC
www.fsc.org
FSC® C015829

# You can be Princess Catherine's Bridesmaid

Piccadilly Press • London

# A Fairytale Romance

**M**any girls dream of one day finding a prince. Lucky Kate Middleton has not only fallen in love with one – but she is also about to be a princess! Kate is an ordinary girl – her mother, Carole, and father, Michael, both worked for an airline, and now run a company selling various items, like balloons and paper plates, for parties. By marrying the Queen's grandson, Prince William, Kate is about to become Princess Catherine and part of the British Royal Family.

*Stick a photograph or draw a picture*
*of the happy couple here.*

# The perfect proposal

Kate and Prince William met after they had finished school, when they were both studying at St Andrew's University in Scotland. After a nine-year romance, Prince William asked Kate to marry him when they were on holiday in Kenya in Africa. He gave Kate the same engagement ring that his father, Prince Charles, gave his mother, Princess Diana.

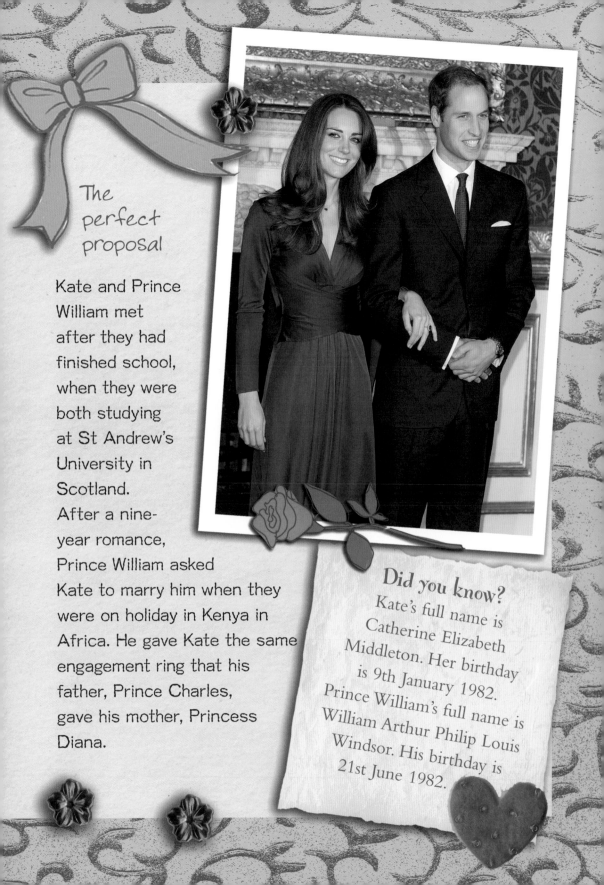

**Did you know?**
Kate's full name is Catherine Elizabeth Middleton. Her birthday is 9th January 1982. Prince William's full name is William Arthur Philip Louis Windsor. His birthday is 21st June 1982.

# Dreams for the Big Day

Every bride has to do a lot of planning to make sure that her wedding is a special occasion and that everything goes smoothly. Kate will have several official organisers and royal advisors to assist her. She will also ask her bridesmaids to help her decide on everything from her dress to the wedding cake. Why don't you pretend you are one of the lucky bridesmaids and help Kate too?

*Draw a picture of you and Kate here.*

## Think of a theme

A bride often chooses an idea to run through the whole wedding, from the design of the invitation and napkins, to the colour of the flowers and table decorations. Sometimes the wedding theme reflects the bride and groom's hobbies.

*Which wedding theme would you choose for Kate and the Prince?*

A ROYAL THEME, like crowns, gold and silver or jewels

A ROMANTIC THEME, like hearts, flowers or butterflies

AN IMAGINATIVE THEME, like springtime, fairyland or under the sea

A HISTORICAL THEME, like Roman feast or medieval banquet

A FUN, FANCY DRESS THEME, like beach party, Disney or Bollywood

### COLOUR SCHEME IDEAS

| Black & White | Ivory & Cream | Pink | Tangerine | Aqua blue | Green | Purple | Chocolate & Cream |

*Use any of the above or think of your own colour and theme*

Write your theme for the wedding here.

Write or design your colour scheme here.

# An
# Important Invitation

Kate and Prince William's wedding will take place on Friday 29th April 2011 – St Catherine's Day! The ceremony will be held at Westminster Abbey in London, which can hold around 3,000 people.

## A golden ticket

Kate and Prince William want everyone to share in their happy day. One hundred members of the public, chosen completely at random, will be sent an invitation to the wedding. Just imagine if one dropped on to your doormat!

## A VIP guest list

Other people lucky enough to be invited to the wedding will include: members of the British Royal Family, Kate's family, Kate and William's friends, members of royal families from overseas, other heads of countries, such as President Barack Obama of the USA and his wife, and celebrities who know the couple and who have worked for charities they support.

# Design Kate's invitations

What do you think the royal wedding invitations should be like?
Decorate the wedding invitation below.

Mr and Mrs Middleton and
HRH Prince Charles and the Duchess of Cornwall
would like to invite

..........................................................

to the wedding of

HRH Prince William Arthur Philip Louis Windsor
to Catherine Elizabeth Middleton

on Friday 29th April 2011
at Westminster Abbey at 11am

R.S.V.P.

- Don't forget to write the name of
  the person being invited!
- R.S.V.P. is French for 'répondez s'il vous plaît'
  which asks you to reply.

# Divine Dress

What sort of dress do you think Kate should choose? Should it be silk, satin or velvet? Slim-fitting, with a full skirt, or a train? Should it have embroidery, crystals, or both? Write or draw your ideas for the perfect dress in this space.

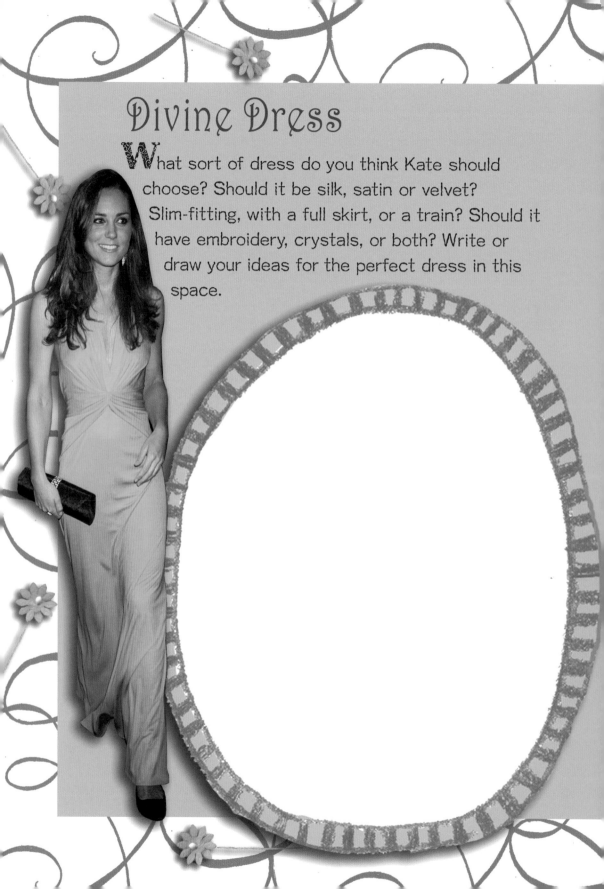

# Heavenly Hair

Kate usually likes wearing her long, glossy, chestnut hair down — even for posh events. But many brides with long hair choose an elegant up-do for their wedding day.

☐          ☐                    ☐          ☐

*Tick which of these hairstyles above you think Kate should go for or draw your own hairstyle below.*

*Don't forget any extra decoration, like flowers or a veil!*

# The Rings and Precious Things

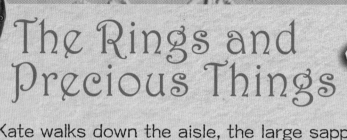

As Kate walks down the aisle, the large sapphire and diamond engagement ring given to her by Prince William will sparkle on her finger.

*Colour it in here!*

## A twinkling tiara

Every princess needs a tiara. The Royal Family may lend Princess Catherine one of their many priceless coronets, or the Queen might decide to give her one to keep, as a wedding present.

*Draw what it might look like.* ➡

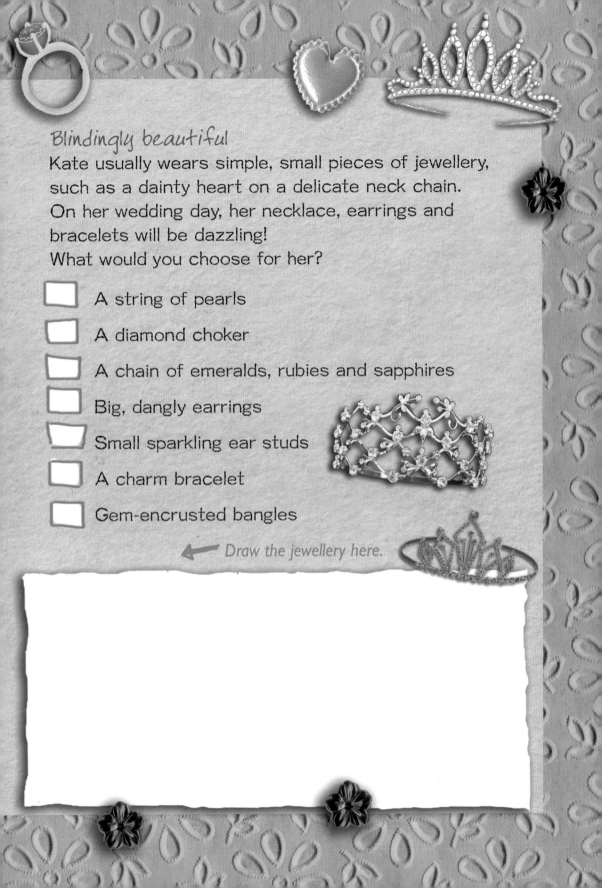

## Blindingly beautiful

Kate usually wears simple, small pieces of jewellery,
such as a dainty heart on a delicate neck chain.
On her wedding day, her necklace, earrings and
bracelets will be dazzling!
What would you choose for her?

- [ ] A string of pearls
- [ ] A diamond choker
- [ ] A chain of emeralds, rubies and sapphires
- [ ] Big, dangly earrings
- [ ] Small sparkling ear studs
- [ ] A charm bracelet
- [ ] Gem-encrusted bangles

← *Draw the jewellery here.*

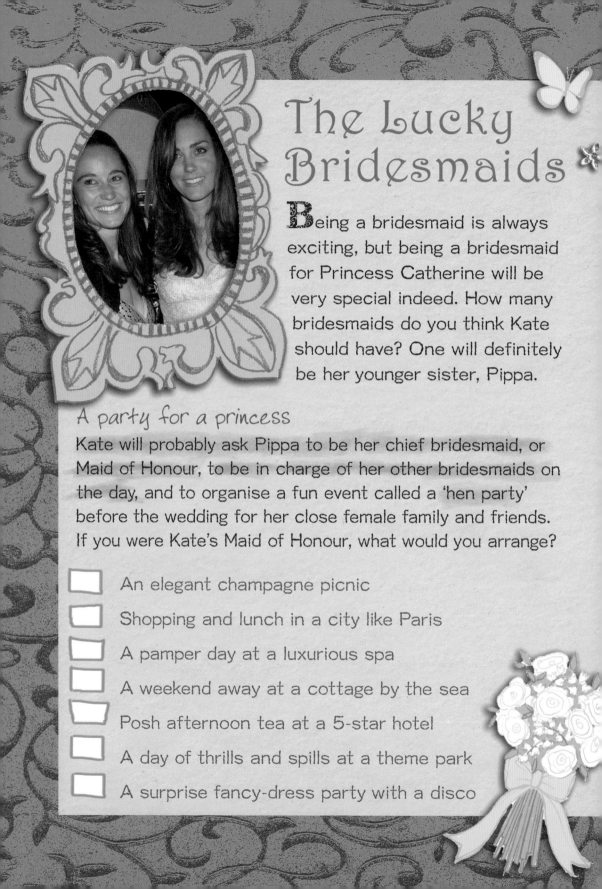

# The Lucky Bridesmaids

**B**eing a bridesmaid is always exciting, but being a bridesmaid for Princess Catherine will be very special indeed. How many bridesmaids do you think Kate should have? One will definitely be her younger sister, Pippa.

## A party for a princess

Kate will probably ask Pippa to be her chief bridesmaid, or Maid of Honour, to be in charge of her other bridesmaids on the day, and to organise a fun event called a 'hen party' before the wedding for her close female family and friends. If you were Kate's Maid of Honour, what would you arrange?

- [ ] An elegant champagne picnic
- [ ] Shopping and lunch in a city like Paris
- [ ] A pamper day at a luxurious spa
- [ ] A weekend away at a cottage by the sea
- [ ] Posh afternoon tea at a 5-star hotel
- [ ] A day of thrills and spills at a theme park
- [ ] A surprise fancy-dress party with a disco

## The all-important outfits

What sort of dress will Kate choose for her bridesmaids? Here are some ideas for you to colour in.

*Draw your perfect bridesmaid dress here.*

## Gorgeous gifts

Kate will give thank you gifts to her lucky bridesmaids.

*Tick or write what she should pick here.*

- ☐ A charm bracelet
- ☐ A locket necklace
- ☐ Glittering earrings
- ☐ A personalised photo frame
- ☐ A little keepsake box

# Fabulous Flowers

The royal wedding will be a festival of flowers. Thousands will be used to make Kate and the bridesmaids' bouquets, buttonholes for VIP guests, and decorations for the church and reception. Kate is getting married in the springtime, so she might choose fragrant spring blooms like freesia, hyacinths and lily of the valley – then her wedding will not only look wonderful, it will smell wonderful too.

## A beautiful bouquet

What should Kate's bouquet be like? Big and bright? Small and stylish? Pale and pretty? Here are some ideas for you to colour in.

## The language of flowers

Since Queen Victoria, royal brides have always carried a sprig of myrtle in their bouquets, as this stands for 'happy marriage'. Kate's favourite flowers are thought to be white lilies, which happen to mean 'majesty'! Here are some other flowers and what they have come to symbolise:

**Crocuses**
cheerfulness

**Daisies**
innocence

**Forget-me-not**
good memories

**Ivy**
friendship

**Purple tulips**
royalty

**Red roses**
'I love you'

## A memory to keep

Ask a grown-up to give you one of the flowers featured in Kate's bouquet, then press it, so you can keep it forever. Here's how:

*Put the flower in the middle of a newspaper and carefully fold it shut. Open a big dictionary or phone book and place the newspaper inside, in the middle. Close the book and pile other heavy books on top, then wait for a week.*

Stick your pressed flower here.

# The Prince and His Men

**A** perfect princess needs a dashing prince. William will wear either a traditional morning suit or his Royal Air Force dress uniform on his wedding day. He would look extremely smart in both – but which do you think he should choose? Colour each outfit in here and tick the one you prefer.

## Royal right-hand men

A bridegroom usually chooses his closest male family member or friend to be his 'best man' – to help him prepare for the event and stand at his side on the day. At royal weddings a 'best man' is called a supporter – and there are sometimes more than one. Prince William will definitely choose his younger brother,

Prince Harry. He may also ask his oldest friends, such as Thomas van Straubenzee or Edward van Cutsem. Other important men at the wedding will be William's father, Prince Charles, and his uncles, Prince Andrew and Prince Edward.

**QUICK QUIZ**

*Do you know Prince William well enough to be a supporter?*
*Test yourself to find out.*

**1.** As a child, Prince William's nickname was: **a)** Dingbat **b)** Wombat **c)** Womble

**2.** Aged 7, William told his mother he wanted to grow up to be:
**a)** a fireman
**b)** a policeman
**c)** a postman

**3.** How tall is Prince William?
**a)** 6 ft 1  **b)** 6 ft 2  **c)** 6 ft 3

**4.** Is Prince William . . .
**a)** right-handed  **b)** left-handed  **c)** both

**5.** What is the name of his black Labrador dog?
**a)** Pigeon  **b)** Widgeon  **c)** Smidgeon

<u>Answers</u>
**5. b)** Widgeon
**4. b)** left-handed
**3. c)** 6 ft 3
**2. b)** A policeman
**1. b)** Wombat

# The Dawn of the Big Day

The night before the wedding Kate will stay at one of the royal family's residences in London, such as Prince Charles's home, Clarence House, or the Queen's home, Buckingham Palace. Imagine how excited and nervous she will be! Maybe she will try to relax with a bubble bath and some beauty pampering. She may get her bridesmaids to advise her what to do.

*Write below what you would suggest to unwind.*

## Getting dressed

It is traditional for a bride to wear or carry something old, something new, something borrowed and something blue. The 'something old' might be her engagement ring. The 'something new' could be her dress. The 'something borrowed' might be her tiara. What would you give Kate for her 'something blue'?

*Draw it here.*

## An exciting journey

Millions of people will line the streets of London to watch Kate travel to Westminster Abbey. After the wedding, Kate will leave Westminster with the Prince in the same glass coach that took William's mother, Diana, to her wedding. In the glass coach, Kate will feel and look just like Cinderella.

*Stick a photo of Kate here.*

# A Special Service

One thousand year old Westminster Abbey is grand and beautiful. Only royalty, plus Abbey staff and certain knights and their families, are allowed to get married there. It is also where British queens and kings are traditionally crowned.

*Inside the abbey*

*Kate and Prince William's families will sit closest to the altar.*

*William will arrive at this entrance to the right of the altar, followed by the Queen.*

Aisle    Choir

Cloister

*Kate will arrive at this entrance with her father. Pippa and the other bridesmaids will join Kate from here as she walks down the aisle.*

## Tying the knot

The marriage ceremony will be conducted by the Archbishop of Canterbury. He will lead prayers and guide Kate and Prince William in saying their vows. The couple will then exchange rings and sign the marriage register. The pair will now be Prince William and Princess Catherine of Wales.

## Practise your curtsy

Before the happy couple leaves the church, Princess Catherine will curtsy to the Queen.

Here's how to do it:

1. Begin by standing straight, feet together.
2. Put one foot behind the other, resting it on the ball of your foot.
3. Bend both knees equally and bow your head.
4. Straighten up and bring your back foot back to where you started.

# Celebrate!

**P**rince William and Princess Catherine have said that they want everyone to share in their happiness, and their wedding day has been declared a national holiday. There will be public and private parties up and down the country – and all over the world. Here are some ways you can join in the exciting occasion.

## Make a sparkly Princess tiara to wear

*You will need:* **5 glittery pipecleaners**

*What to do:* **Join the pipecleaners by twisting their ends together to create one very long pipecleaner. Measure about 12 cm from the left end, then make a smallish loop, twisting it once at the bottom so it stays firm. Move a couple of centimetres to the right and make another loop. Continue making loops until you are about 12 cm from the right end.**

**Ask a grown-up to help you make your tiara fit your head by wrapping the straight ends around each other into a circle of the right size.**

You can stick sequins on with glue for extra sparkle.

## Royal refreshments

Here's how to make some celebration food and drink.

Princess Pink Punch: Float frozen strawberries and raspberries in pink lemonade or strawberry milk.

Romantic Royal Sandwiches and Pizza: Use a heart-shaped cookie cutter to serve sandwiches and pieces of pizza in special shapes.

Pink Princess Popcorn: Melt some white chocolate and add a couple of drops of red food colouring until the mixture is pink. Sprinkle some popcorn over a tray lined with greaseproof paper. Then drizzle the pink chocolate mixture over it and put the tray in the fridge until the chocolate is hard. Enjoy!

## Congratulations!

Make a wedding congratulations card for Princess Catherine and Prince William of Wales. You could always make up a poem to go inside it!

# Party Time!

After the ceremony at Westminster Abbey, Prince William and Princess Catherine will ride in a golden carriage through the streets of London, lined with thousands of cheering well-wishers, to Buckingham Palace. Here they will appear on the balcony so the crowds below can wave and take their photograph.

*Stick a photo of this here.*

## A stunning banquet

Around five hundred special guests will arrive for the wedding reception. Massive long tables will be lined with golden chairs, and decorated with silver candlesticks and cutlery, crystal goblets and gorgeous flowers. Heralds trumpeting fanfares will introduce toasts and speeches to the happy couple. There will be at least ten courses to eat – but what food and drink would you have on the menu?

*Using blank card, create a menu fit for a Prince and Princess!*

## Cutting the cake

Every bride and groom wants to have a wedding cake that not only tastes special, but looks special too. They cut into it together, while their guests clap and cheer. Royal wedding cakes usually have four or even five tiers and stand at over 1.5 metres tall!

*This was the cake for the wedding of Prince Charles to Lady Diana.*

What do you think Prince William and Princess Catherine's cake will be like? *Draw it here.*

# Happily Ever After

It is traditional for a bride and groom to take a holiday – a honeymoon – after their wedding. Where do you think the royal couple will go? They may return to Kenya in Africa, where they got engaged. They might spend time in Scotland, at one of the Queen's homes, Balmoral Castle. Or they may go somewhere else in the world.

*Write here what you think they might put on a postcard home.*

## Post Card

Home sweet home
Prince William and Princess Catherine will return from their honeymoon to live at their cottage on the island of Anglesey. Whenever in London, they will stay in an apartment at St James's Palace.

## Work and family

Once married, Prince William will continue to work in the RAF as a search and rescue helicopter pilot. He will continue many royal duties, with Princess Catherine by his side, such as public appearances and charity work. The couple would also love to have children.

*Write how many children you think they will have and the names they will choose here.*

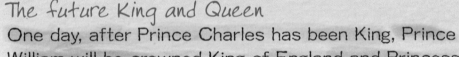

## The future King and Queen

One day, after Prince Charles has been King, Prince William will be crowned King of England and Princess Catherine will become Queen.

*Design a crown for each of them here.*

# Happy Memories

**N**o one will ever want to forget the wedding of the century. Fill in the spaces here, to help you remember the very special event forever.

*Stick your favourite photo or draw a picture of the wedding here.*

I watched the wedding of Prince William and Princess Catherine at _____

I was with _____

I wore _____

It was a special day for me because _____

I thought that Princess Catherine looked _____

My favourite bit about the whole day was _____

_____

_____

_____

The thing/s I think should have been different was/were _____

_____

Other people thought that _____

_____

The souvenirs I have of the day are _____

_____

In the future, I hope that Prince William and Princess Catherine

_____

If I met Prince William and Princess Catherine I would say

_____

Other things I will never forget are

_____

Today's day/month/year:

_____ / _____ / _____

*Stick a photo, or draw a
picture, of you celebrating
the royal wedding here.*